GREAT
BRITISH
TRACTORS

GREAT
BRITISH
TRACTORS

A Pictorial History

MIRCO DE CET

AURA

This edition published in 2014 by Baker & Taylor (UK) Limited,
Bicester, Oxfordshire

Copyright © Arcturus Holdings Limited
26/27 Bickels Yard, 151–153 Bermondsey Street
London SE1 3HA

ISBN: 978-1-78404-293-6
AD003572UK

Printed in China

Contents

Introduction

I t is truly moving to read about the experiences of farm labourers and farmers before the Industrial Revolution. Before the 1800s, people farmed mainly with hand tools, usually crafted from iron by the local blacksmith. They were simple tools and using them would have been tedious, difficult and could quite often result in dreadful accidents. The working day started at the crack of dawn and ended well after the sun had set. These would have been long, hard and extremely tiring days.

In our modern age of mechanization and hi-tech machinery, it is difficult to imagine what this must have been like. Farmers and labourers must have been grateful when agricultural tools were finally modified so they could be efficiently pulled by animals. The draught horse was an extremely strong and powerful animal, specifically bred for hard and heavy tasks such as ploughing and farm work. A team of these horses could pull ploughs in a way that a team of men could never have achieved.

Yet the farm labourer was still indispensable. Although the horses pulled the ploughs, the farm worker had to control the horse, make sure the plough was at the right depth in the soil and, most importantly, check that the furrows were straight. This method of farming endured long after the development of the modern tractor; even in the early 1900s, oxen and mule teams could still be seen pulling carts and ploughs.

With the advent of the Second Industrial Revolution in the 1860s, tools and machinery became even more sophisticated and adaptable. New horse-drawn machinery began to appear – first the reaper and then the combine, which was able to cut and thresh fields of grain all at the same time. On the positive side, this new machinery meant that farm work could be carried out using less manpower, and was made easier and more efficient. On the other hand, there was less demand for labourers on the farms, and many suddenly found themselves out of work.

During the final decades of the 19th century, the British farming industry also experienced a period of depression and many farm labourers were forced to move to the growing cities in search of new jobs. However, innovations in tractor technology continued.

With the invention of steam came the traction engine and with the advent of the combustion engine came the tractor as we know it today. These machines gave an incredible advantage to the farmer and as they became more and more sophisticated they became more productive and were able to carry out an abundance of jobs. Today, tractors are multifunctional pieces of machinery, with a single person able to control implements that cater for most of the work that needs to be carried out during the different seasons of the year.

And, even now, new technology is being used to make the tractor and other farm machinery more efficient and productive. Satellite navigation, robotics and self-drive tractors are no longer ideas for the future. Instead, they have become a reality of today.

1

The Heavyweights

Something like the modern tractor first appeared in the USA during the late 1800s. But the word 'tractor' was not a term that would have been generally used for this type of vehicle at the time. The origins of the term 'tractor' are a little murky... some say that it was an amalgamation of 'traction' and 'motor', used by the sales manager of the Hart-Parr company, W. H. Williams, in 1906. Others would dispute this and say that, in fact, the word appeared some years earlier. It seems that a man by the name of George Edwards from a small town in Illinois, USA, may well have used the term in 1890. After obtaining several patent approvals for tracked vehicle designs, he created a machine which, on a sketch dated 16 April 1890, is clearly labelled 'Tractor'! Whichever is correct, both in America and in Britain these

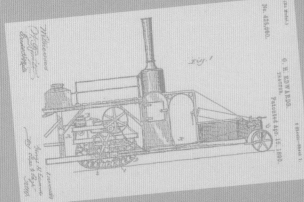

Ploughing became much easier when the steam engine acquired wheels and became mobile. This photo from 1910 shows a horse-drawn water tank standing by to replenish the engine.

machines were originally static and towed from venue to venue to carry out different types of farm work. Once in place they would be attached, via their drive belt and pulley, to another piece of machinery, such as a log cutter or thresher. The steam engine would activate the secondary machine and allow the necessary work to be carried out much quicker.

But it wasn't long before someone put wheels on their static steam engine and gave it traction. From then on huge, steaming traction engines could be seen roaming the British countryside!

The Robey Portable

The image to the right shows a typical portable steam engine. This particular one is made by Robey, a company that produced thousands of engines from the 1850s right up to the 1950s. Many were exported to Australia, but this one was sent to Northern Ireland where it was used in a quarry before being shipped to Scotland for restoration.

1925

Marshall, Sons & Co.

Built in 1925, this is 'Florence', Marshall, Sons & Co.'s portable steam engine number 79936.

Horse Power v. Steam Power

Thomas Aveling was the first person to supply traction to the wheels of a portable engine in 1858. While experimenting with a Clayton & Shuttleworth engine, Aveling fitted a chain from the crankshaft to the rear axle of the machine, so the action of the crankshaft could activate the back wheels. Although this sounds very straightforward you can't imagine the problems it encountered before it became a success!

Traction engines were originally used for hauling wagons on roads (where the going was good). But by the later part of the 19th century these huge machines would become much more widespread as more companies began to build them and they became an established part of farming machinery.

It took a while for steam traction engines to be accepted by farmers and, even when they were, it was not a natural transition. Horses and other animals were still used extensively. Although traction engines were capable of doing much of the work that the animals could do and in a much shorter space of time, they also had their drawbacks. Because they were extremely heavy, the machines were poorly suited to working on very soft or hard ground and their agricultural use was often limited to pulling other farming equipment. They were also expensive to run – they had to be steamed up in the morning, fed fuel throughout the day and then steamed down after the day's work. Even after all that, you still had to clean the beast!

John Fowler & Co.

John Fowler & Co. was based in Leeds and produced traction engines and ploughing implements. This Fowler ploughing engine, 'The Chief', was built in 1874, has a single cylinder and produces some 14 horsepower. When he was experimenting with using the traction engine for ploughing, Fowler first tried a single engine. But he found that, even though it was more expensive, two engines stationed either side of a field, with a plough running between them, was a more satisfactory system. Note the cable used for towing the plough, situated below the boiler.

Hornsby-Akroyd

The Hornsby-Akroyd Safe Oil Traction Engine, built in 1896 by Richard Hornsby and Sons of Grantham, Lincolnshire, was regarded as the first commercially successful British tractor, and the company planned to manufacture it with a choice of engines. It is uncertain how many were actually made and what configuration they took – but we know that three were shipped to Australia and one is still resident in England.

The Marshall Traction Engine

This Marshall traction engine goes by the name of 'Pearl' and was built in 1906. It was shown on the Marshall stand at the prestigious Smithfield show. Originally sold for £493 to an agricultural machine owner, it was then registered to Hampshire County Council. In 1921 it was registered for road use and took on ploughing, threshing and road-making duties. It was requisitioned by the Hampshire Agricultural Executive Committee during the Second World War and used for threshing and wood cutting. Recently overhauled and restored, 'Pearl' is now displayed at many agricultural shows around the UK.

Charles Burrell & Sons

Built in 1919, this Charles Burrell & Sons engine was specifically ordered and constructed for Mr C. H. Parsons, a contractor of St Columb Major in Cornwall. The engine goes by the name of 'Cornish Maid' and is an agricultural traction engine. It has an extra-long boiler and connecting rods, a solid disc flywheel, three-speed gears, is fully sprung and weighs 11.5 tons. It is the only one of its kind in the world!

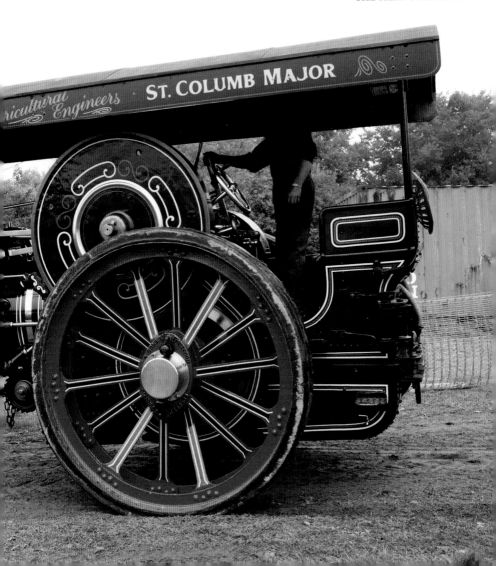

McLaren

This McLaren ploughing engine was built in 1919 and named 'Hero'. It is a monster of a traction engine. Although 'Hero' is marked as weighing 14 tons on the front, this was only added to allow it to pass over bridges that had weight restrictions – it actually weighs 22 tons! 'Hero' could be one of the largest – if not the largest – steam plough engines in existence.

Clayton & Shuttleworth

Clayton & Shuttleworth was originally established as an engineering business by Joseph Shuttleworth and Nathaniel Clayton at Stamp End Works in Lincoln in 1842. Three years later the company started producing portable steam engines, and went on to make threshing machines and traction engines. The Clayton & Shuttleworth general purpose engine shown left goes under the name of 'Elizabeth'. Built in 1919 it has a single cylinder which produces 7 nhp (nominal horsepower).

William Foster & Co.: Tank Makers

An agricultural machinery company based in Lincoln, William Foster & Co. Ltd dates back to 1846, when William Foster purchased a flour mill in Lincoln. Ten years later he converted his premises into an iron foundry and engineering shop. Here he began producing grinding mills and then progressed to manufacturing threshing machines, chaff-cutters and portable steam engines. The engineering shop became the original Wellington Foundry. During the First World War the company was partly responsible for producing the first tank. The emblem of a tank is clearly marked on the smoke box door shown right.

1931

The 'Sir William'

These photos show the traction engine known as 'Sir William' powering a Foster threshing machine. This is one of the last remaining 8-nhp, single-cylinder, general purpose agricultural engines produced by William Foster & Co. Built in 1931, it was very popular with threshing contractors due to its efficiency and power, which allowed it to drive not only a threshing drum but also a full-size stationary baler.

John Fowler & Co.

John Fowler & Co. was based in Leathley Road, Leeds.
The company produced traction engines, ploughing
implements and equipment and railway machinery. John
Fowler was an agricultural engineer and inventor who
pioneered the use of steam engines in farming, and has
been credited with the invention of steam-driven ploughing engines. 'Tommy', the engine featured here, was built
in 1922 and spent most of its life with its first owner in
Oxford, where it was used for threshing and
baling work.

1931

Ransomes, Sims & Jefferies

Ransomes, Sims & Jefferies was a major British agricultural machinery maker. It produced traction engines, trolleybuses, ploughs, lawn mowers, combine harvesters and tilling equipment, as well as manufacturing aeroplanes during the First World War. Traction engine 'Sister Wendy' was built in 1931 and is a 9-ton, single-cylinder, 6-nhp engine. It was first exhibited at the RASE (Royal Agricultural Society of England) show in Warwick.

CHAPTER

Trailblazing Tractors

While monster steam traction engines lumbered across the fields and countryside, there were pioneering designers hard at work, aiming to make the tractor smaller, more reliable and more user-friendly. Although these vehicles would be more compact and agile, they would still need to have the power to pull ploughs and activate other farm machinery.

It was the advent of the internal combustion engine that allowed this change to happen. Nikolaus Otto invented his four-stroke engine in the 1860s and by the early 1900s machines appeared with new internal combustion engines. Innovations such as these allowed the tractor to become lighter and more reliable. There was also no need to steam up in the morning and steam down in the evening.

Above: John Froelich fitted a vertical, single-cylinder petrol engine to the running gear of a hybrid steam traction engine. The Froelich machine is considered to be the first tractor in the world that used an internal combustion engine.

Opposite page: In November 1901, British inventor Dan Albone produced his prototype for a tractor powered by a petrol engine. The Ivel Agricultural Motor was a three-wheel machine.

Some of these early machines used a variety of fuels – anything from gas and coal to oil distillates and even turpentine.

Many farmers were reluctant to leave steam behind, but it soon became clear that the internal combustion engine was the power-source of the future. The fact that oil products such as petrol and paraffin were now widely available also helped its expansion in the market.

Ivel

This Ivel is often seen at tractor events around Britain. As demonstrated here, the little engine can still successfully be used for ploughing.

1902

Ivel

The engine of the Ivel is water cooled –
note the big grey water tank at the rear.
A friction clutch and a chain-drive
assembly transmitted power to the
rear wheels.

Ivel

Power	6 kW (8.0 hp)
Weight	403 kg
Maximum load	2540 kg (2.5 tons)
Maximum speed	5 mph (8.0 km/h)
Engine size	2900 cc (177 cubic inches)
Cylinders	2
Stroke	4

Above: Specification for the Ivel Agricultural Motor of 1902.

Below: Dan Albone sits proudly on his Ivel, and shows how versatile his invention is. Spectators watch with excitement as he demonstrates how the machine can effortlessly work a binder.

Saunderson

The Saunderson Tractor
and Implement Company
was founded in 1890
by H. P. Saunderson
and based in Elstow,
Bedford. Saunderson
travelled to Canada and
visited the Massey and
Harris companies just
prior to starting up his
own business. A failed
'self-moving vehicle' was
demonstrated in 1898, but
by the early 1900s the
company was producing
three-wheel, multi-
purpose tractors. These
were joined in 1910 by a
four-wheel version, some
of which had Crossley
engines – Crossley
would eventually buy
Saunderson out in 1924.

1912

MOGUL
25 H.P.

Mogul

The International Harvester Mogul 12-25 weighed nearly 5 tons, but when it was built in 1912 it was actually lighter and a lot less clumsy than the machines that had preceded it. Gone was the chain-style steering. The bodywork not only covered the engine – the tractor also had a cab to keep the farmer dry in the winter and in shade in the summer. In fact, the machine looked quite like an automobile! The engine was an opposed twin-cylinder unit and ran on kerosene with a carburettor for each cylinder. All in all this was a much more advanced machine than anything previously produced, so much so that International Harvester of Great Britain sold around 340 units at £500 each.

Mogul

The Mogul 8-16 was presented in 1914 and was a new lighter-weight tractor from the International Harvester Corporation. Only a small number of these machines were released that year, but they clearly marked a new path in the design and appearance of the tractor. There was a single-cylinder engine that produced 16 flywheel horsepower and the small twin wheels up front allowed the machine an incredible turning circle, which suited the needs of many farmers.

CHAPTER 3

During the First World War (1914–1918) demand for efficient farming machinery sky-rocketed. Food production and agriculture were essential to the war effort at home, but tractors also had a part to play on the front line.

In 1915, the War Agricultural Executive Committees were set up by the British government. These organizations were tasked with increasing farming production and

1910s–1940s:
Boom & Bust

managing the country's limited agricultural wartime resources.

At this time, much of Britain's farming was still done manually and with animals. Although tractors were available on the market, they were only bought by the few who could afford them and recognized them as a necessity. Therefore, it was down to the government committees, in conjunction with local councils, to distribute more tractors and increase food production. This was partly done by dictating land usage and advising which crops would be grown. Tractors also started to be imported from America, where there was an abundance of new machines.

1914–18

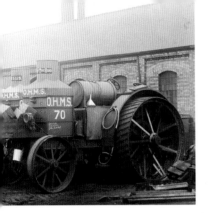

Trench-crossing Tractors

The First World War was brought to a stalemate by trench warfare. Something had to be done to avoid the mass killing of soldiers as they charged out of their trenches into bullet-riddled battlefields.

One idea that Fosters had been experimenting with was developing a tractor – in this case a heavily modified Daimler-Foster 105 hp tractor – that could cross a typical-sized trench, a requirement laid down by the government's Landships Committee. Soldiers would be protected by the cab of the tractor and thus be able to advance successfully, without being gunned down by enemy fire. This innovation would also help soldiers to cross muddy ground and enemy trenches.

Sadly, the experiment came to nothing, although the unmodified tractors continued to tow huge naval guns and other military equipment throughout the war. However, it was an early step towards designing the first military tank.

The Holt Tractor

The American inventor Benjamin Holt began experimenting with tracked vehicles in the early years of the war, and built the Holt 75 in 1914. The Holt 75 was used by the British, French and American armies, mainly for hauling heavy artillery. By the end of the war around 10,000 of these vehicles had been produced. The tractor used both tracks for steering, had a maximum speed of 15 miles per hour (24 km/h) and was powered by a petrol engine. After the war, Holt joined forces with Daniel and C. L. Best to create the Caterpillar Tractor Co., which remains one of the world's leading engine manufacturers.

1914

L. J. Martin Overtime Tractor Company

The American Waterloo Boy Tractor was imported to Britain by the L. J. Martin Overtime Tractor Company. The tractors arrived in Britain dismantled and the company reassembled the machines, before selling them on to their clients. The vehicle used a two-cylinder horizontal engine and produced 24 horsepower.

51

The Massey Ferguson Story

A Brief Encounter with Harry Ferguson

Harry Ferguson was born in the small Irish town of Growell, County Down, in 1884. Before getting into farming, he dabbled with building aeroplanes, inspired by the exploits of the Wright Brothers. He and his brother wasted no time and they constructed an aircraft in 1909. On the day that they were due to make the first flight, the machine was towed through Belfast and up to Hillsborough Park. Although initial attempts to make the plane fly were unsuccessful, on 31 December they took to the skies, watched by a small array of people, including local newspaper reporters. Harry Ferguson had made the first flight ever in Ireland and was the first Briton to build and fly his own plane. No mean feat!

As if that wasn't enough, Ferguson also went on to design the Belfast Plough, which he intended for use with his Eros tractor, a conversion of the Model T car. Sadly the whole venture came to nothing as Henry Ford exported several thousand Model F tractors to the UK, which were cheaper and more advanced than the Eros. Ford of course was also on the verge of building a new factory in Cork, where he would manufacture the Model F.

On the basis of this, Ferguson decided to design a new plough specifically for the Fordson Model F. This resulted in his most famous invention in 1926 – the Ferguson three-point hitch!

A year later, Ferguson also developed 'draft control', which automatically adjusted the depth of an implement by measuring how much force was needed to pull it through the soil.

Below: The press and local farmers watch as Ferguson demonstrates his three-point hitch.

Opposite centre: Ferguson with his aircraft.

Ferguson then decided to design a new type of tractor, which would use a Hercules engine and a David Brown gearbox. It would also be fitted with all the new equipment he had invented. The tractor became known as the 'Black' Ferguson.

First, he needed to find a company that could produce the tractor in great quantities. It was the David Brown Company that came to his aid, and the tractor's colour was changed to battleship grey.

The American market was Ferguson's next goal and he set off across the Atlantic to meet Henry Ford in 1938. After watching Ferguson demonstrate his machine, Ford agreed to build the tractor. However, the initial prototypes that Ford produced were not to Ferguson's liking and he returned to America to oversee proceedings himself – the eventual result was the 9N. This time Ford got it spot on and used all the newest production techniques to create the tractor to Ferguson's specifications, though the final model was fitted with a Ford engine rather than a Hercules.

Left: The Black Ferguson being demonstrated to journalists.

Below: The original Ferguson Brown was manufactured in 1936 and used a Coventry Climax engine.

Below: The infamous meeting between Harry Ferguson and Henry Ford, where their agreement was supposedly sealed with a gentlemen's handshake!

1946

In 1947 Henry Ford II took over the reins at the Ford factory and decided he wanted to terminate the Ferguson agreement – all ties were severed a year later. A dispute began between the two men and it resulted in a court battle, with Ferguson being awarded a large sum of money.

Ferguson had already struck up an arrangement with Sir John Black of the Standard Motor Company in Coventry, who agreed that Ferguson would look after design, development, sales and service, while the Standard Motor Company would build the tractor. The result was the TE20 and with it began the story of the incredible 'Little Grey Fergie'. The first machine rolled off the Banner Lane production line on 6 July 1946. It used an American Continental Z-120 engine until the 2088cc Standard Vanguard engine replaced it in July 1948.

The Ferguson Company eventually merged with the Massey-Harris Company in 1952 and Ferguson's legacy to tractor manufacture lives on today in the Massey Ferguson brand.

Left: The original Ferguson TE20 with Continental engine.

Top: 1953 diesel version known as the TEF20.

Massey, Harris and Ferguson

In 1890, the success of Alanson Harris's open-end binder prompted Canadian business competitor Hart Massey to propose a merger. On 6 May 1891 the two companies became one, under the name of Massey-Harris Company Ltd. Some smaller agricultural companies were also bought up by the corporation during the next few years, and this helped to increase the new company's versatility and product range.

The First World War started in 1914 and the tractor became essential to the Canadian war effort. As a member of the British Commonwealth, Canada had troops fighting in Europe. Since there were fewer men to work on the land

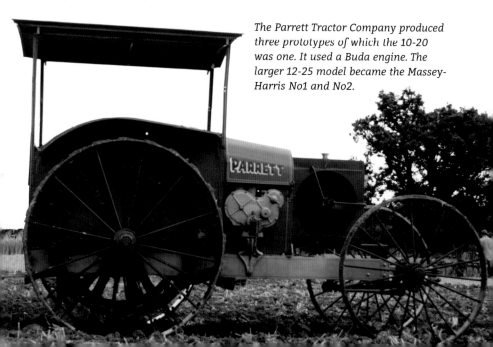

The Parrett Tractor Company produced three prototypes of which the 10-20 was one. It used a Buda engine. The larger 12-25 model became the Massey-Harris No1 and No2.

Hart's father, Daniel Massey, founded the family business in 1847

Alanson Harris

the demand for efficient tractors increased; a tractor was able to cover more work in a day than a man and his horse could cover in a week.

However, although Massey-Harris was a leading manufacturer of farming equipment, it had not yet produced a tractor.

So, in 1917, the company started to search for a model that could be imported into the Canadian market. After a deal with the Bull Tractor Company fell through, Massey-Harris made a new agreement with the Parrett Tractor Company

of Chicago in 1918. Dent Parrett drew up designs for three models – the MH1, MH2 and MH3 – and production started in 1919 at the Massey-Harris engine factory in Toronto.

Despite being well-made machines, they dated quickly and were made redundant by the new, lighter models coming into the market. Having now burnt their fingers twice, Massey-Harris decided to wait and see what further developments would take place within the tractor industry, which was growing at a rapid pace.

As the world economy started to recover in the mid 1920s, Massey-Harris looked for a new partner. They chose the J. I. Case Plow Works Company of Racine, Wisconsin, and in 1927 they acquired the company. Although Massey-Harris bought the Case company, it sold back the rights to the Case name. What they were really interested in was the 'Wallis family' of tractors, which were well known both for their excellent fuel efficiency and their distinctive U-frame construction.

Massey-Harris continued to produce Wallis tractors and made the old Case factory in Racine their own. For the first time, they were in a position to infiltrate the American market.

The current Wallis tractor, the 20-30, continued to be manufactured and several new

When Massey-Harris bought the J. I. Case company, their interest was the Wallis tractor, which was known to be reliable and well-built.

tractors followed as well, along with the first true Massey-Harris, the General Purpose machine.

Produced at a time when the farming community was suffering the effects of the Great Depression, the GP tractor failed to sell, even though it was a very efficient machine. Further models came and slowly the company established itself with some exciting and reliable machines.

Back in the 1940s, Massey-Harris had turned down an offer from Harry Ferguson to produce his TO20, equipped with all his advanced attachments. Ferguson took his tractor to America where he struck a deal with Henry Ford instead and both companies reaped the rewards. By the time that Ford and Ferguson went their separate ways, Ferguson had already built up a large distribution network in America and he used this to sell his newly imported TE20 tractor, which had been launched in England back in 1946.

The Massey-Harris general purpose machine was not a great success but it was brimming with potential and new ideas.

Production was not something that Ferguson enjoyed and he started looking for someone to take over that side of the business. Conveniently, Massey-Harris were looking to make a similar kind of arrangement. The two signed a deal in 1953, in which Massey-Harris bought out the Ferguson Tractor Company. The name was changed to Massey-Harris-Ferguson, which was later shortened simply to Massey Ferguson.

Initially both brands produced their own tractors and much upgrading happened throughout the next few years. The new tractors were painted in red and grey livery, with the Massey-Harris red and yellow livery relegated to the archives.

In 1959 the company bought the respected Perkins Diesel Engine

The Massey-Harris Junior (left) was introduced in 1939. This used the old paintwork of red and yellow, whereas the Massey Ferguson 35 (right) has the newer paintwork of red and grey to denote the Ferguson connection.

Company of Peterborough and, in doing so, became builders as well as suppliers of engines. New 100 series machines – the 135, 150 and 165 – were manufactured in Britain and France while the larger machines were assembled in the USA.

The booming sales period of the 1970s was followed by a sudden reversal in fortunes during the 1980s and Massey Ferguson found the going hard. They were running short of operating capital and eventually, in 1993, AGCO acquired the rights to Massey Ferguson.

Massey Ferguson's Banner Lane plant in Coventry was threatened with closure when AGCO executives warned that the company would pull out of Britain if the country stayed out of the euro.

Production ceased at the Banner Lane works in 2002 and the 4300 model became the last series to roll off the production line. The announcement of the factory's closure, with the loss of a thousand jobs, was a major blow to manufacturing and the economy both locally and nationally. Only the Coventry office remained as the corporation's headquarters.

1915–22

International Harvester

International Harvester's Titan 10-20 was manufactured between 1915 and 1922. It had a massive 8.7 litre, two-cylinder engine which ran on kerosene. Despite facing competition from the all-conquering Fordson, the Titan held its own. By reducing the price and offering buyers incentives such as a free plough, the Titan survived throughout the war years, until the company introduced a newer model in the 1920s.

Minneapolis-Moline

The shortage of British tractors just prior to and during the war saw many different companies from America send their machines to the UK. The Minneapolis-Moline company was one of them. Shown here is the company's 1916 Universal Model. It was considered to be the first real row-crop tractor. Its advertising noted, 'One man cultivates two rows at a time with the Moline.'

1917–28

Fordson

The Fordson Model F was the world's first mass-produced, affordable tractor. Henry Ford had experimented with several prototypes before coming up with the Model F, and when it finally hit the market the machine sold like hot cakes. It was easy to use, sold at a competitive price and consequently appealed to many farmers. The vehicle was way ahead of anything else on the market; what Ford had done with the Model T automobile he now did with the tractor.

The tractor rolled off the production line at a hurriedly built factory in Michigan and went on sale in October of 1917, selling for $750. The original Fordson used a 20-horsepower, four-cylinder vaporizing oil engine. In its early years the Fordson gained a reputation for being unreliable, but any defects were soon ironed out and, by mid-1918, more than 6,000 Fordson tractors were in use in Britain, Canada and America.

The agricultural economy was seriously hit by the recession of 1925. As a consequence, the Ford Motor Company ended its US tractor production and sales in 1928 and transferred manufacture to Cork, in Ireland, the following year. Production was later moved to Dagenham in Essex.

1917–28

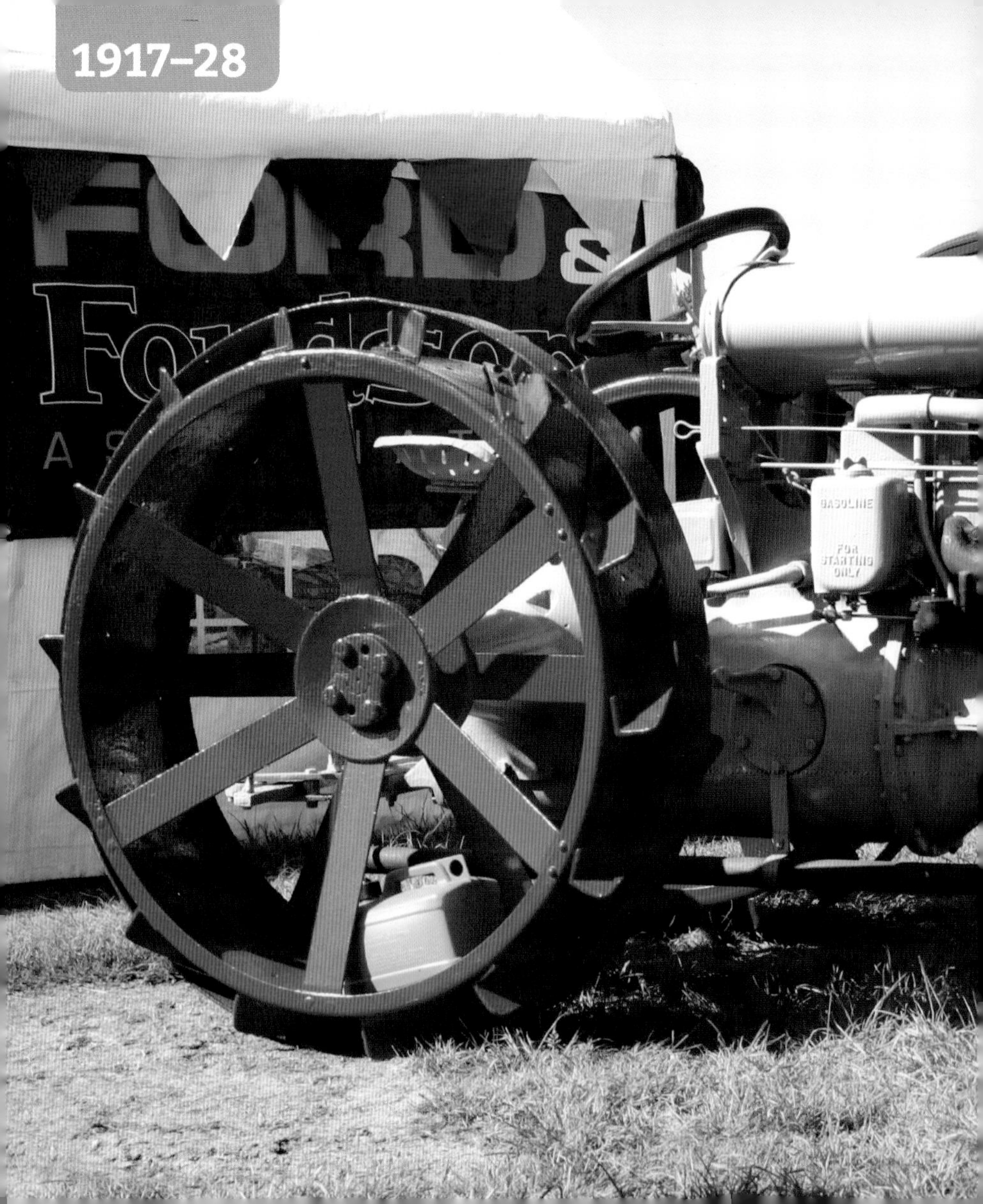

Fordson

The Ford Motor Company's shareholders had no interest in tractor production, so Henry Ford started an independent company for building tractors, named Henry Ford & Son – a.k.a 'Fordson'. The Fordson Model F tractor was produced between 1917 and 1928. The engine was a four-cylinder, side-valve unit which produced 20 horsepower.

International Harvester 8-16

With its all-enclosed bonnet and seating position, the International Harvester 8-16 could be mistaken for an automobile. This tractor was produced between 1917 and 1922 and used a 4.6 litre, four-cylinder engine which ran on kerosene. It was presented as a new lightweight tractor and became extremely popular when it was introduced to the British market in 1919.

Alldays & Onions

Alldays & Onions are not well known for tractor building. They built automobiles between 1898 and 1918, and were based in Birmingham (UK). Their tractor, known as the Alldays General Purpose Tractor, used an internal combustion engine which was discreetly enclosed by the bodywork. Behind this was a canopied cab, which gave the driver some protection from the elements.

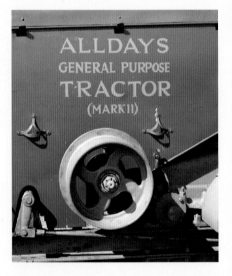

Case

In 1918, adverts for the latest Case tractor asked the viewer to 'study this plan view of the new Case 10-18 kerosene tractor'. What it highlighted in detail was the chassis, showing the farmer just how many of the tractor's parts were easily accessible.

Maintenance costs were always a concern and Case cross-motor tractors were fitted with a much stronger chassis to combat what was known as 'frame whip'. This occured when the frame became bent under pressure. During this period, many manufacturers were looking at different ways to combat this problem.

1919

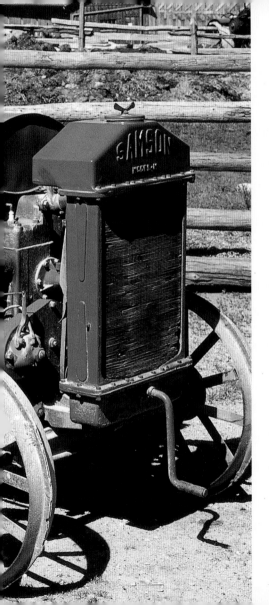

The Samson Model M

William Durant, chairman of General Motors Corporation (GMC), had seen the success of Henry Ford's Fordson tractor and decided he wanted to enter the tractor market. In 1919 GMC bought out the Janesville Machine Company and the Samson Sieve-Grip Tractor Company of Stockton, California. They called the new group the 'Samson Tractor Company Division of General Motors Corporation' and began operating on 1 May that year.

GMC continued producing the Samson Sieve-Grip model until announcing the new Samson Model M. This tractor was priced at $650 and was equipped with mudguards, a governor system, belt-pulley and other extras that were not included on the Fordson.

Unfortunately, due to a very competitive tractor market, financial losses and a change of corporate direction, the Samson division was closed in 1923.

Austin

Herbert Austin, of
the Austin Motor Co.,
Birmingham (UK) is
best known for his
automobile and truck
business, but he was
also responsible for
designing a tractor. He
became the first British
manufacturer to adopt

unit construction, which meant that he used the engine, gearbox and transmission as the backbone of his vehicle.

The Austin tractor experienced some teething problems and it was also much more expensive than its rival, the Fordson. As a consequence, it was not a great success; when the First World War ended the company commenced production of the famous Austin 7 automobile, and tractor production was moved to France.

Peterbro

The Peterbro tractor was manufactured by Peter Brotherhood Ltd., of – unsurprisingly – Peterborough. It used a four-cylinder engine and produced 29 horsepower. The Peterbro's engine was fed a mixture of petrol and paraffin. Built in 1920, it was well made and came with extensive maintenance instructions, which stated that the 'appearance of the machine also reflects on the operator'. No pressure then!

Below: A Peterbro with an added cylindrical gas conversion. These sorts of modifications were not unusual at the time.

The "PETERBRO"

18-35 H.P. AGRICULTURAL TRACTOR

Manufactured by

PETER BROTHERHOOD LTD.

Engineers

PETERBOROUGH :: ENGLAND.

THE PETERBRO TRACTOR

MANUFACTURED BY

Peter Brotherhood, Limited,

PETERBOROUGH.

Smithfield Show Stand No. 2

BRONZE MEDAL, LINCOLN, 1920.

For use with Howard Ploughs, Cultivators, Knapp Drills, Garrett Threshers, and other Farm Implements.

AGRICULTURAL & GENERAL ENGINEERS, Ltd.

CENTRAL HOUSE, KINGSWAY, LONDON, W.C.2.

ASSOCIATING :

Aveling & Porter, Ltd. (Rochester).
Barford & Perkins, Ltd. (Peterborough).
E. H. Bentall & Co., Ltd. (Heybridge).
Blackstone & Co., Ltd. (Stamford).
Peter Brotherhood, Ltd. (Peterborough).
Charles Burrell & Sons, Ltd. (Thetford).
Burrell's Hiring Co., Ltd. (Thetford).

Clarke's Crank and Forge Co., Ltd. (Lincoln).
Davey, Paxman & Co., Ltd. (Colchester).
Richard Garrett & Sons, Ltd. (Leiston).
James & Fredk. Howard, Ltd. (Bedford).
L. R. Knapp & Co., Ltd. (Clanfield).
E. R. & F. Turner, Ltd. (Ipswich).
A. G. E. Electric Motors, Ltd. (Stowmarket).

Above right:
Early Peterbro adverts.

The Peterbro was designed to last and was extremely well made. It received many awards and was reputed to be the highest grade tractor of its power brand ever built. Despite – or perhaps because of – all these attributes, the tractor was considerably more expensive than its rivals. Many farmers were unwilling (or unable) to purchase a Peterbro when they could buy a Fordson for considerably less.

Caterpillar

The Caterpillar Sixty was manufactured between 1925 and 1931. As its name suggests, it was a 60 horsepower crawler. Before the merger between the C. L. Best Tractor Company and the Holt Manufacturing Company, the tractor was manufactured as the C. L. Best 60 Tracklayer – it was the most successful tractor in the Best model line.

This machine is a rather special Sixty because it was never actually put into production. Caterpillar experimented with several engines and designs before launching their diesel Sixty (far left). This was one of the prototypes – it uses an Atlas Imperial engine.

Allis-Chalmers

The Allis-Chalmers Model U was sold as the United Model U between 1929 and 1931. It was originally distributed by the United Tractor and Equipment Corporation, but when they went out of business Allis took it over as the Model U. It continued in production until 1952.

The Allis-Chalmers Model U was never a great tractor, but it was an innovative one – the first to be provided with rubber tyres.

Harry Merritt, Allis-Chalmers' Tractor Division general manager, was largely responsible for pioneering the use of this material. Merritt's acquaintance with Harvey Firestone, the founder of the Firestone Tire

and Rubber Company, was probably useful too. Merritt carried out experiments on a local farmer's Model U and discovered that rubber tyres produced far superior results to steel. Still, the transition from steel to rubber didn't happen overnight – many farmers remained sceptical about its durability, and rumours circulated that the material could poison crops.

Fordson N

The Fordson N was a replacement for the Model F and production started in Cork, Ireland before moving to Dagenham. Assembly commenced in 1929 and continued until 1954. Several variations were produced during that period – the 9N, 2N, 8N and NAA. The Fordson N played a major role during the Second World War, helping British farmers to increase production when the supply of food from abroad was halted due to German U-boat raids.

The Fordson Model
N Standard was fitted
with a 27 horsepower,
four-cylinder engine,
a high-tension ignition
system for improved
starting and – unlike
its predecessor – rear
mudguards.

The Great Slump

By the beginning of the 1930s, the economic situation in the UK was looking grim and what would be known as the 'Great Slump' was making its mark on the agricultural industry. The Great Depression – which had started in America in 1929 – had spread across the water and factories and businesses were feeling the economic downturn in Europe.

The effects of the First World War had lingered on in Britain where – unlike in America, Canada and Australia – there had been no boom time. It was a difficult period; in some areas of the country as much as 70 per cent of the workforce was jobless, and thousands of families were on the poverty line.

By the late 1930s, the prospect of yet another war was looming large. Yet, as German troops marched into Austria, British prime minister Neville Chamberlain told the farming community that he was reluctant to stop the large-scale imports of food – some 65 per cent – from abroad. Britain, he assured the farmers, was not going to war. Most farmers were baffled by this and felt that Britain should be making urgent preparations to increase its food production. As one rural commentator remarked: 'It takes as long to rear a bullock as it does to build a battleship!'

Bristol

Bristol of England made small crawlers
for use on farms and in market gardens.
These were initially produced at the Douglas
Motorcycle Works, which supplied the
horizontally opposed, twin-cylinder engines.

In 1948 came the introduction of the new
Bristol 20, which incorporated the rubber-
jointed track system. The engine produced
22 horsepower from either a petrol or TVO
Austin 2.2 litre OHV engine.

1936

Ransomes, Sims & Jefferies

The Ransomes name and origins can be traced back to Robert Ramsome, who built an ironworks in Norwich in 1789. In the early part of the 20th century the company became Ransomes, Sims & Jefferies Ltd., and produced a variety of machinery, including steam traction engines.

The MG2 crawler was introduced in 1936 and used a single-cylinder, 600cc, air-cooled Sturmey Archer engine. It had a single-speed gearbox and a roadless track system. It was replaced by the MG5 and production ceased in 1948.

1932–38

Farmall

The Farmall F-12 was introduced in 1932 by the International Harvester Company (IHC) and production lasted until 1938. In this time a staggering 123,442 were built in the USA and a further 2,848 in Germany. The numbers speak for themselves: it was an extremely popular tractor both in the USA and abroad. This model was eventually superseded by the more powerful F-14, but visually they were very similar.

1939

Case

The Model D series of Case tractors with a new slimline design was first manufactured in 1939. There were various designations and they could be distinguished from earlier models by their Flambeau Red colour scheme. This is the DEX model, which became popular in Britain as a result of the Lend-Lease agreement with America during the Second World War.

David Brown Ltd.

After the falling-out with Ferguson, David Brown started developing its own tractor and launched the VAK 1 in 1939. With its four-cylinder, water-cooled engine (petrol or petrol/TVO), and its one reverse and four forward gears, the model proved an immediate success.

The company purchased a redundant textile factory at Meltham Mills in Huddersfield prior to the Second World War, with the intention of building tractors there. But as the war progressed more important materials had to be manufactured, such as munitions and aircraft parts. Modified VAK 1 aircraft tugs and crawlers were also used for the war effort. After the war, VAK 1 production continued and in 1945 the VAK 1A was introduced with several additions and improvements.

McCormick-Deering

The International W-30 was a hard-working tractor and was used to power other machinery (such as combines), as well as to plough. It used a four-cylinder, 4.6 litre engine and was made between 1931 and 1939.

Farmall

In 1939 International Harvester introduced its smallest tractor yet. It was aimed at the farmer with a small farm who still needed a tractor that could carry out a multitude of tasks. The compact Farmall Model A was just perfect for the job!

Farmall

Unlike the Farmall A, the M was a much bigger and more powerful machine altogether, capable of pulling a three- or four-bottom plough. Introduced by International Harvester in 1939, it was superseded by the Super M in 1952.

4

The Golden Age and After

When the Second World War started in 1939, Britain was better prepared than it had been in 1914, and the government immediately took control of agricultural production. The 'County War Agricultural Executive Committees' – or 'War Ags' as they were called – decided who would grow what and organized the distribution of food throughout the country. A rationing system for the public was put in place and farmers were given a fixed price for their produce. With the Battle of the Atlantic seriously affecting British imports, and German U-boats enforcing a naval blockade, supplies to Britain were dangerously low and more food had to be grown at home.

The 'War Ags' controlled the tractors and implements that

ON HIS MAJESTY'S SERVICE

OFFICIAL PAID

Your Ration Book
Issued to safeguard your food supply

HOLDER'S NAME AND REGISTERED ADDRESS

Surname CHURCHILL

Other Names WINSTON. L. S.

Address 10 Downing Street
SW1

NAT. REG. NO. AYUV 295 1

Date of Issue - 7 JUL 1941

Serial Number of Book

PT 496809

If found, please return to

CITY OF WESTMINSTER.
FOOD OFFICE.

R.B.1 [General] 4

Above: The Fordson Model F was one of the most popular tractors during the 1920s and 1930s, and it also played a key role during the war years.

Opposite page: Rationing was strictly governed to make sure everybody got a fair share; even the prime minister had a ration book. Rationing in Britain continued after the war, formally ending in 1954.

were being used. Machines were leased to farmers in an attempt to better equip them and enable them to grow more produce.

Although the Fordson N was the preferred machine, tractors were also imported from America as in the First World War, this time through a Lend-Lease agreement set up between the British and American governments. Once again, American tractors were seen in the fields of Britain helping farmers with their duties.

Land Girls

The Women's Land Army (WLA) had been introduced during the First World War and was re-established at the start of the Second World War in 1939. The organization was set up to fill the jobs left vacant by male labourers, who had been sent away to fight. Women of all ages were asked to volunteer, although later the WLA used conscription to boost numbers. Many of the members had never driven a car before – let alone a tractor – and prospective drivers had to take a proficiency test before they were allowed behind the wheel. Operating a tractor took skill and a lot of elbow grease. The machines were started by cranking a handle at the front – if done incorrectly, this could break your arm.

Members of the British Women's Land Army harvesting beets. A woman is driving a Fordson tractor in the foreground, while three others with pitchforks are loading the beets on to the trailer behind.

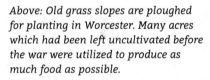

Above: Old grass slopes are ploughed for planting in Worcester. Many acres which had been left uncultivated before the war were utilized to produce as much food as possible.

Left: Soldiers in Northern Ireland are seen working with a Fordson, harvesting a ten-acre field of oats. Many British soldiers were released for temporary emergency farm work and helped to ease the farm labour shortage.

113

John Deere

The mid-1930s was not a good time for the agricultural industry, with the Depression hitting many farmers and manufacturers. Despite this, John Deere decided to launch their new Model A, a specific row-crop machine, which had adjustable rear wheel track and the company's signature small twin wheels at the front. It was very popular and Deere followed it up with a smaller machine, the Model B.

These two streamlined tractors were styled to Henry Dreyfuss' now classic design. The models were also equipped with six-speed gearboxes in 1940. There were, of course, several variants of the Model A – the AR, for example, was the standard track model.

Minneapolis-Moline

The Minneapolis-Moline tractor company was created in 1929, through the merger of the Moline Implement Company, the Minneapolis Threshing Machine Company and the Minneapolis Steel & Machinery Company.

When the Second World War broke out the company sent tractors to Britain to help with the shortage of machinery and to increase food productivity, through the Lend-Lease agreement.

The Model GT used the Minneapolis-Moline Model LE four-cylinder engine and was a standard tread machine. With some slight changes this later became the GT-A, which continued in production through to 1947. That same year the GTB was announced and an LPG Model later followed.

Like many vehicle manufacturers during the war, Minneapolis-Moline also made ammunition and parts for tanks and ships in their factories.

Minneapolis-Moline

Minneapolis-Moline introduced the U series in 1939. Starting with the basic U Model it extended through the UTU row-crop, with its small double-front wheels, the UTS standard tread and, of course, the UDLX and UOPN 'Comfotractors' – the first came with a cab and the other was a roadster! Not all of these tractors were imported to the UK during the war, but many of the UTS models could be seen working in British fields.

Minneapolis-Moline

The Minneapolis-Moline
Model Z series was first
produced in 1936, and took
over from the Model J.
It used a four-cylinder,
water-cooled engine and had
a five-speed gearbox. Again,
there were several versions to
choose from, depending on
the type of farm work that
was required.

1937

Oliver

The Oliver 70 was produced in 1937. It built on the success of the Oliver Hart-Parr 70, but was equipped with a new, streamlined body.

The company did away with the name 'Hart-Parr' and from then on was just known as 'Oliver'. The 70 was available in several versions including row-crop, as shown here.

McCormick-Deering

Introduced between 1940 and 1953, the McCormick-Deering W9 was a standard-tread tractor built at International Harvester's factory in Milwaukee. The tractor was imported into Britain to help with the war effort as part of the Lend-Lease agreement signed between Britain and America.

There were six models in the 9 line-up – W9, WD9, WR9, WDR9, I-9 and the ID-9. The last two were industrial models, and the WDR9 was a rice model, with a hand clutch for changing gear while standing. It could also be distinguished by its wider mudguards. Two engines were available; both were International Harvester four-cylinder 5.5 litre units, but the buyer could choose between petrol or distillate.

Allis-Chalmers

Introduced in 1940, the Allis-Chalmers Model C was an upgraded version of the Model B, which had been a huge success for the company since its launch in 1937. The Model C was a row-crop machine and used a four-cylinder engine with a displacement of 125 cubic inches.

David Brown

During the Second World War, the engineering company David Brown principally manufactured gears. These gears were intended for tanks and other military vehicles. The company also continued to make tractors for the military, including this VIG 1 'tug', which was derived from the VAK 1, the company's original tractor. Very different from the VAK 1, it was used for towing aircraft and bomb trolleys and was an extremely powerful piece of kit.

1940s

PERKINS LTD. PETERBOROUGH.
MADE IN ENGLAND
L. 4. DIESEL ENGINE

FOR INFORMATION   ALWAYS QUOTE ENGINE
REGARDING MAINTENANCE   NUMBER WHEN
REFER TO INSTRUCTION
LITERATURE   ORDERING SPARE PARTS.
   ENGINES ARE NORMALLY SET FOR SEA LEVEL WORKING
AND SHOULD BE DE-RATED FOR ALTITUDE OPERATIONS.
       PATENTED GT. BRITAIN 541400.

FORDSON
MAJOR

Fordson

The son of a farmer, Henry Ford was no stranger to the agricultural industry. He started experimenting with tractor designs as early as 1906, and several odd machines followed, including a modified Model T Ford.

Ford's first real tractor was the Model F, which he produced in 1917.

In 1945 came the E27N, manufactured in Dagenham and essentially an updated version of the Model N. The machine was becoming more sophisticated every time it was updated. It was produced in four different versions, each with varying specifications. The engine was an in-line, four-cylinder, side-valve unit, and a diesel version was also made available in 1948.

Marshall, Sons & Co.

Field Marshall tractors were manufactured by Marshall, Sons & Co. of Gainsborough, Lincolnshire. A Field Marshall could be distinguished quite easily because it emitted a 'thudding' noise and the whole machine moved back and forth on its chassis. It was very different to other tractors and used a two-stroke engine attached to a large flywheel. The design was reportedly copied from the Lanz machines which were very popular on the continent at the time, although the Lanz used a 'hot bulb' engine.

Starting the early machines was a test of patience, skill and, quite often, energy. The machine was started up by inserting a smouldering piece of special paper containing saltpeter (sodium nitrate) into the cylinder head via a special screw-in holder. The flywheel was turned to the centre, with any luck the engine would fire and, hopefully, the tractor would start! Easy to describe, trying to actually do it can be a little more tricky!

The Series 1 Field Marshall was made from 1945 to 1947, when it was superseded by the Series 2.

1947–49

Marshall, Sons & Co.

The Field Marshall Series 2 was manufactured between 1947 and 1949 and was a great improvement on the Series 1. These tractors were very popular and were mainly used for hauling farm machinery, particularly threshing machines.

The tractor was connected to the thresher via a 'belt pulley', a large, flexible belt that was stored near the engine, and acted as power plant during operations. The picture below shows a Field Marshall 2 and its belt pulley in action.

Marshall, Sons & Co.

The Series 3 Field Marshall was a bigger tractor and, once again, an improvement on the previous model. Manufacture started in 1949 and the tractor was fitted with a modern six-speed gearbox. A series 3A was introduced in 1953. To the dismay of many Marshall tractor owners, some were painted orange; several farmers were so disgusted they returned their tractors to have them painted the 'proper' Marshall green!

Post-War Britain

The tractor had played a major role in keeping food on the table during the Second World War and the post-war period turned out to be a golden age for the tractor industry. The machines that had been so faithful and seen so much use during the war years were now ready to be replaced, and there was certainly no shortage of choice.

In post-war Britain, the farmer was not just looking for a new tractor, but also for exciting innovative designs which would allow him to cut down on his labour costs and crucial overall expenditure.

These dreams had become real possibilities; new implements were being introduced into the market that allowed the farmer and his tractor to carry out much of the work that had previously been done by farm workers. Although the late-1940s and 1950s was a period of high yield, this was achieved with a much smaller workforce than previous decades.

New tractors, companies and a considerable amount of consolidation led to thriving sales. Not only were the bigger manufacturers competing for customers, there were some smaller manufacturers too, all keen to promote their products.

American manufacturers like Allis-Chalmers had also decided to move into Britain, setting up manufacturing bases and importing parts from America, which were then assembled in the UK. The choice of tractors and the implements to go with them seemed endless.

It was not just American firms getting in on the act. Manufacturers on the Continent were not going to let this boom pass them by, and several models from Italy, Germany and France could be seen in the post-war fields of Britain too. At the same time that tractors from around the globe were hitting British shores, Britain was also exporting tractors and machinery worldwide; it was a truly busy time for the farming industry.

1947

Massey-Harris

The Massey-Harris Pony was initially introduced in France to serve farmers with small farms. It started life with a Continental petrol engine but a diesel was added later too. Launched in 1947, it was never a great success.

Allis-Chalmers

After the Second World War, Allis-Chalmers made the decision to manufacture tractors in a factory in Southampton. Initially the parts were shipped in and the machines were assembled like kits, but after a while parts were sourced locally. A factory was set up in Leicestershire and the machines became totally UK-built.

The first tractor built by the company in Britain was the Model B, and it quickly became a favourite with farmers. It was small, light and affordable, and remained in production until 1957.

1946

Ferguson

Following the split between Ferguson and Henry Ford II, Ferguson looked around for a new partner to help develop his tractors. That partner came in the form of the Standard Motor Company, Coventry. Its managing director, Sir John Black, struck up a deal with Ferguson in which the company would build the tractor and Ferguson would look after the design, development, sales and service side of the operation. The result was the Ferguson TE (Tractor England) 20. The first unit came out of the factory at Banner Lane on 6 July 1946. The original version used a Continental engine, but this was later replaced with a Standard Vanguard unit.

Ferguson

Several versions of the famous little Grey Ferguson were produced, such as the TED, which was a much thinner tractor and ideal for vineyard work. The TED version could be run on TVO, but it was happier starting on petrol.

Ferguson

It was 1947 when the Continental engine was replaced with a 24-horsepower Standard Vanguard car engine, and the tractor was given the designation TEA 20. There was such a demand for this little tractor that production had to be stepped up in 1948, increasing volume to over 5,000 units per month.

David Brown: Tractor Dynasty

David Brown was founded as far back as 1860 and made wooden gears for the textile industry in Britain. By the 1930s they had become the largest UK-based manufacturer of gears. It was in the mid-1930s when they became involved in the tractor business, collaborating with Harry Ferguson on the Ferguson Brown tractor in 1936. This tractor started life at the company's Huddersfield factory but production was eventually moved to a dedicated tractor factory at Meltham Mills, West Yorkshire. A disagreement with Ferguson led them to build their own tractor, the VAK 1. It was due to be manufactured before the Second World War, but had to be put on hold because of war work. The VAK 1 finally went into production after the war and sold extremely well.

The Cropmaster

The David Brown VAK 1 tractor progressed through its development stages and in 1947 reached the designation VAK 1C, also known by its much more familiar name, the 'Cropmaster'. The tractor had a good variety of standard accessories, including headlights. The 'Cropmaster' was made from 1947 to 1953, a long production period for a very popular tractor.

The David Brown 25D tractor had a four-cylinder, liquid-cooled unit that could run on diesel, petrol or kerosene. The tractor was manufactured from 1953 to 1958.

The slightly larger 30D model was manufactured for one year less, ending production in 1957. It used a slightly more powerful engine and, like the 25, had four cylinders that could run on petrol, diesel or kerosene.

International Harvester

The huge International Harvester Company built a factory in Doncaster in 1946, initially to build agricultural implements. It then progressed to manufacturing tractors in 1949, the first of which was the McCormick-International Farmall M Model, to give it its formal name.

The International B-275 was manufactured at the Doncaster plant from 1958 to 1968. The engine was an International unit designated IHGB BD-144, which produced 35 horsepower. The transmission had eight forward gears and two reverse. Over 54,000 tractors were manufactured, many of which are still around today.

1958

Turner Yeoman

Several new makes of tractor were introduced into Britain during the 1950s, and none was stranger than the 'Turner Yeoman of England', which hit the market in 1958. Based on a marine model, its diesel engine was designed in a V-4 configuration. Although this was a well designed and comfortable machine to drive and use, it suffered from mechanical problems. It was also rather pricey compared with tractors of similar capability built by the mass-market manufacturers.

David Brown

Launched in 1956 at the prestigious Smithfield Show, the David Brown 900 couldn't help but catch the eye. The in-house 'hunting pink', along with the added blue radiator and wheels, was undoubtedly attractive, and it was the only model to use these colours. Buyers could choose which engine fuel they preferred – petrol, diesel or paraffin. The 900 was superseded in 1958 by the 950.

Fordson

The Fordson New Major E1A series of tractors, manufactured from 1952, was the last to bear the Fordson badge. From 1961 the British and American companies would be amalgamated, use one Ford badge and move to a grey-and-blue colour scheme.

The New Major's four-cylinder engine could run on a variety of fuels, with the diesel versions being easy to start and maintain while also being very reliable. But this was a big machine and farmers were looking for something smaller. Enter the Dexta in 1957...

Dexta

Powered by a 30.5 horsepower, three-cylinder engine, the Fordson Dexta was a completely new design, intended to compete directly with the Massey Ferguson 35. The diesel tractor was generally favoured over the petrol tractor. Besides the regular version there was also an industrial model, which had mudguards at the front as well as the rear (as shown here). In Germany you could even buy a Dexta Special, made specifically for the German market.

1950s

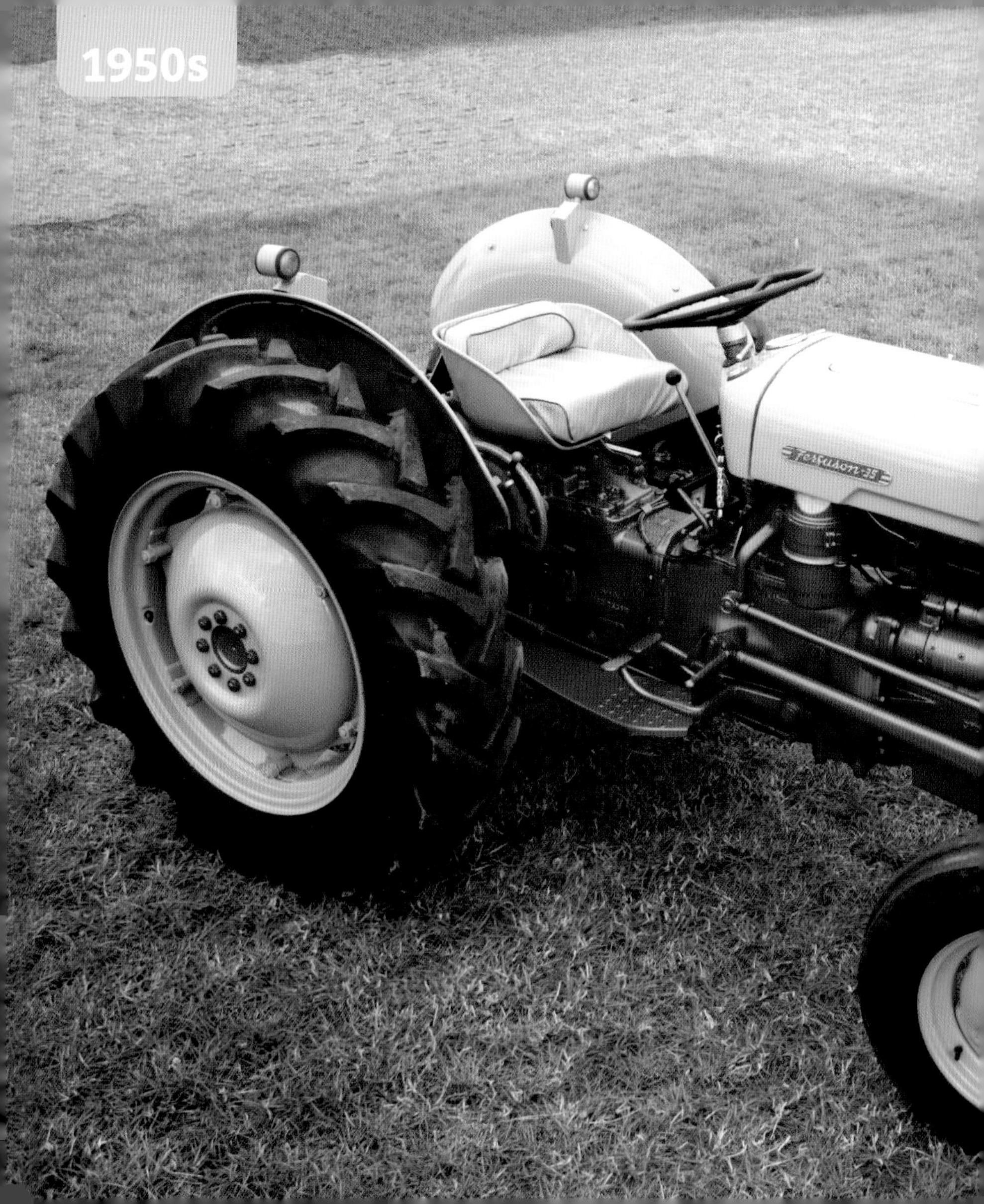

Ferguson

The TE 35 was developed by Ferguson but then taken over by Massey-Harris when the companies merged. After that, it wasn't long before the machine was repainted in the new corporation's colours of red and grey.

International Harvester

Manufactured in Britain between 1961 and 1966, the International B-414 could be purchased as a diesel or petrol tractor. The petrol version, made mainly for the American market, had a four-cylinder, 2.3 litre, liquid-cooled unit. The diesel example used the International Harvester BD-154 engine, which also had four cylinders and was liquid cooled. In 1966 this model gave way to the International Harvester 434, which had been available in America since 1964.

Nuffield

In 1946 the chairman of Morris Motors announced that Nuffield were going to start making tractors. The company commenced tractor production in 1948 with their Nuffield Universal.

About twenty years later they introduced the 10 series, commencing manufacture in 1964. The bigger of two machines was the 10-60, which basically stood for 10 gears and 60 horsepower, (this is how the tractors were designated). The tractor was equipped with a BMC four-cylinder, 3.8 litre diesel engine.

Nuffield tractors continued to be manufactured under their own name until 1969, when they became part of the Leyland Motor Corporation, took on the Leyland name and were given two-tone blue paintwork.

Massey Ferguson

The MF35 and MF65 got a complete makeover in the early part of the 1960s. They became known as the MF135 and MF165 – the 'Big Red Giants' – and were the first in the new 100 series. While the bodywork styling changed quite dramatically – to a very angular, sharper look – not too much changed as far as the engines were concerned, and the faithful Perkins diesel or Continental petrol units were both available.

Allis-Chalmers

Sadly the ED-40 was the last Allis-Chalmers tractor to be manufactured in Britain. It never sold terribly well and was heavier than its predecessor, the D272. It used a standard Ricardo 2.3 litre engine and had an eight-speed transmission. Four thousand units were manufactured, some of which went to America, with production ceasing in 1968.

Massey Ferguson

The Massey Ferguson 35 is possibly one of the best-known tractors of all time. Its history is both intriguing and interesting. It started life as the Ferguson TE 20 (Little Grey Fergie), developed into the Ferguson FE35 and finally became the Massey Ferguson 35 when the companies merged.

John Fowler & Co.

The Track Marshall Crawler tractor was produced by John Fowler & Co. and was a tracked version of the Field Marshall Tractor, which was built by Marshalls of Gainsborough (things can get complicated sometimes!). As its name suggests, the Track Marshall 55 had a 55 horsepower Perkins diesel engine.

Ford

The Ford 3000 was produced in several countries; models were marked with either an A (Belgium), B (England) or C (America) prefix to their serial number. The UK tractors were made at the Basildon plant between 1965 and 1975 and used a Ford 2.9 litre, three-cylinder diesel or petrol engine.

David Brown

The David Brown 885 was in production when Case (Tenneco) took the company over. In fact, the Case name is placed on the tractor bonnet next to the David Brown name. While it was marketed as a David Brown in England and built at the Meltham Mills factory, it was sold in America as a Case.

The tractor used a 2.7 litre, three-cylinder David Brown engine, with a choice of either petrol or diesel fuel.

DAVID BROWN

1986

Massey Ferguson of England

The ground-breaking Massey Ferguson 3000 Series was launched in 1986. This was a new advanced group of machines that included electronic controls. They ranged from the 63-horsepower 3050 through to the 173-horsepower 3690. The series was replaced by the Massey Ferguson 6100 series and the MF 8100 series in 1995.

Ford

The Ford 7840 was one of the last tractors to be made under the Ford name. The Ford tractor division was sold to FIAT in 1991 and after 1999 FIAT were obliged to drop the Ford name, which was then replaced with 'New Holland'.

The 7840 was manufactured in Basildon, Essex in 1991 and was fitted with a Ford six-cylinder 6.6 litre engine. It was followed by the New Holland 7840. Essentially, it was the same tractor but with a bit of badge engineering going on.

Ford

Manufactured between 1983 and 1990, the mighty Ford TW-15 used a Ford six-cylinder 6.6-litre engine. With sixteen forward and four reverse gears, it could tackle most jobs around the farm.

Fendt

Fendt have a history that goes back
to the 1930s when their first tractor,
the 'Dieselross', was produced. Since
then they have become renowned
for their stepless Vario transmission
system, as used on this 700 series
model, launched in 1998.

5

Mergers and Takeovers

The landscape in which tractor manufacturers operate today has shifted. Yet although many of the tractors in this chapter are sophisticated hybrids produced by international conglomerates, these machines remain the backbone of the UK's farming industry. At the same time, it is important to remember that a great number of these modern designs were inspired by the work of early British pioneers.

The recession that gripped Britain in the 1980s wreaked havoc on the tractor business and saw the larger manufacturers consume some of the smaller, struggling brands. This eventually led to the creation of the elite group of companies that now dominate the world's tractor and farm machinery market.

The huge AGCO Corporation have Massey Ferguson, Caterpillar, Fendt and Valtra as their core tractor business. Similarly, CNH Global NV is formed of Case IH and New Holland, which, in turn, was a merger of Fiat and Ford. SAME Deutz-Fahr has a pretty impressive line-up too, with SAME, Deutz-Fahr, Lamborghini and Hürlimann tractors making up their numbers. ARGO tractors

Above: An AGCO (Allis-Gleaner Co.) tractor which is painted in the familiar Allis orange colour. AGCO have taken over Massey Ferguson, Fendt and Caterpillar and are now a world leader in the production of tractors.

SpA incorporates Landini and Valpadana and acquired the McCormick name along with the Doncaster factory in 2001.

Although not on quite the same scale as these giants, J. C. Bamford (JCB) is a British manufacturer of agricultural and construction machinery with a prestigious history behind it. Claas, who bought out the Renault tractor concern during the 2000s and who only recently entered into tractor production, is also making itself known worldwide. The past few years have also seen tractors arriving in Britain from countries like India, China and Belarus, all vying for a place in the global agricultural market.

The John Deere Connection

The John Deere Company has a history that can only be envied. The company was founded in 1837 when John Deere, a blacksmith based in Illinois, fashioned a polished-steel plough that could cut clean furrows through the sticky Midwest soil. Since then, the company has grown and prospered into one of the world's leading manufacturing companies.

In 1918, Deere bought the makers of the Waterloo Boy Tractor and produced their first machine, the 25 hp Waterloo Boy. This model was sold in the UK under the Overtime name and played a major part in keeping food on British tables during the First World War.

Through the terrible decline of the late 1920s and 1930s, Deere was one of only a handful of companies to survive. This was a time of 'consolidation' yet Deere was one company that dominated most product categories.

During the 1940s John Deere did its bit for the war effort, making military tractors, ammunition, aircraft parts and cargo and mobile laundry units. At the end of the Second World War Deere also supplied three-wheel, high-clearance tractors to East Anglia under the Lend-Lease agreement. In the 1950s, the company produced its first diesel tractor, the Model R.

John Deere Limited – the UK and Irish branch of the company – was established in 1966. In 1970 the company was awarded the Royal Warrant as suppliers of agricultural equipment to the Queen and, since then, it has grown to be one of the biggest tractor suppliers in the UK and Ireland.

Sales exceeded all expectations during the 1970s, but this was followed by the huge recession in the late-1980s and early-1990s. Like many agricultural companies, Deere suffered and sales of products took a dive.

However, the following year the economy started to grow and over the next few years Deere acquired several other companies, mergers which made the brand stronger and more versatile. Since 2000 the company has branched into new markets, launching facilities in Russia, India and China, and acquiring and setting up joint ventures with a variety of global brands.

Today, John Deere tractors remain a familiar sight in British fields. Their green livery can be spotted from miles away. As of 2012, they were the best-selling tractors in the UK market for 15 years, with around a third of all sales.

CASE, Brown, New Holland & CNH

The massive CNH corporation has many historic tractor names under its belt, including British brands such as David Brown. The group's connections with the UK date back to 1972, when Case acquired David Brown's tractor division.

Established as a pattern manufacturer in 1860, David Brown first ventured into tractor production in 1936 when the company worked with Harry Ferguson to produce the Ferguson-Brown tractor. David Brown quickly gained a reputation for its innovative designs and grew to be one of the

largest British tractor manufacturers of the post-war period. However, the company struggled to repeat its early successes and by the early 1970s a sale to the American company, Case, was on the cards.

The story of the Case corporation began in 1842, when pioneering manufacturer Jerome Increase Case founded the 'J. I. Case Company'. In 1865 Case adopted its eagle trademark – which was based on 'Old Abe', the emblem used by Company C of the 8th Wisconsin Regiment during the Civil War –

and this remained the company logo for the next seventy-five years. In 1869 'Old No.1' – the first Case steam engine – appeared mounted on wheels and pulled by a team of horses. The first Case traction engine was produced in 1876.

Following the purchase of David Brown, Case and its parent company, Tenneco Inc., acquired parts of the International Harvester agricultural equipment operation – after 1985 the letters 'IH' were added to the 'CASE' logo. Although Case now represented a truly international group of tractor brands, the company maintained a footing in the UK. In 1997 Case introduced its new range of MX tractors and moved part of its production to Doncaster. Two years later, the Case Corporation merged with New Holland to create CNH. New Holland celebrated fifty years of tractor production at their Basildon plant in Essex in 2014.

Landini

Founded in the Reggio Emilia province of Italy in 1884, Landini is the oldest established tractor company in Italy. Landini sales are spearheaded in the UK by AgriArgo. From its purpose-built headquarters in south Yorkshire it ensures that dealers have direct access to thousands of Landini and McCormick products and provides on-site technical training.

McCormick

The McCormick Company was founded by Cyrus Hall McCormick in the 1840s. It has a long and illustrious history, as well as a solid presence in the UK. McCormick became one of several companies that amalgamated, back in 1902, to create the International Harvester Company.

In 2000, the Doncaster plant was purchased by ARGO SpA of Italy, which announced that it would become the global headquarters for McCormick Tractors International Ltd. In addition, products from Doncaster would be sold worldwide under the McCormick brand name.

Kubota

Although the Kubota Corporation started life in 1890, its tractor production is a much more recent development. The company's British headquarters in Oxfordshire serves its UK and Irish markets and several major innovations have been introduced by Kubota UK since the 1970s. These include: the first four-wheel drive compact tractor;

the first hydrostatic transmission systems for compact tractors; the first power steering system fitted to 19 hp and 45 hp tractors; and the development of Bi-Speed Turn. In 1996 Kubota UK Limited was awarded ISO 9002 accreditation for its quality systems. As of 2014, Kubota remains the best-selling compact tractor in the UK.

Zetor

Founded in 1946, Zetor has become one of the largest tractor manufacturers in Europe. Originating from Brno in the Czech Republic it produces affordable, well-made tractors which can undertake most jobs on the farm and in the field. The company designs and manufactures most of its own components, including its fuel-efficient engines.

Zetor was not only the first tractor company to manufacture a fully integrated safety cab with insulated, rubber-mounted suspension, but it also produced the first hitch hydraulic system, known as 'Zetormatic', back in 1960. These tractors are rugged and tough and they remain firm favourites with British farmers.

SAME Deutz-Fahr

It was in 1927 when one of the world's first tractors powered by a diesel engine was introduced by Italian Francesco Cassani – the little two-stroke, 40 hp Cassani. The Cassani brothers could hardly have dreamed how their small company would expand.

In 1942 SAME (Società Accomandita Motori Endotermici) was founded by Francesco and his brother Eugenio. In 1952 the world's first four-wheel-drive tractor, the DA 25 was introduced.

Although the company had a tough time to begin with, once established it negotiated some impressive purchases: in 1973 it acquired Lamborghini Trattori, in 1979 the Hürlimann company and in 1995 the Deutz-Fahr company of Germany.

The company is a truly worldwide concern and is involved in ventures in China and Turkey. While SAME tractors have been used in UK fields for a number of years, today more and more British farmers are embracing these versatile and reliable machines.

Hürlimann

Based in the Yorkshire Dales, the trading company Tunstall Tractors
has used Swiss-built Hürlimann machines as its core product since
1983. Hürlimann tractors, first manufactured in 1929, are perfect for
local farmers, who tend to manage smaller livestock farms – most of the
tractors supplied by Tunstall are in the 85–100 hp range.

Lamborghini

Lamborghini tractors may not have the charisma of the company's exotic sports cars, but they are rugged and versatile pieces of machinery, which many UK dealers – such as J. E. Rees in Wales – favour.

Named after its founder, Ferruccio Lamborghini, the Lamborghini Company was building successful tractors long before it turned its hand to sports cars.

Lamborghini was born into a farming family. When he returned from the Second World War, he dabbled with converting old Morris military engines into tractors, for which there was a great demand at the time.

It wasn't too long before Lamborghini Trattori SpA was established in Cento, not far from Bologna in Italy. By 1969 the factory was too small and a further move was required to cope with the increase in demand. This move took place in 1971, by which time Lamborghini was the third-bestselling tractor in Italy.

After a large order from a Bolivian company fell through in 1972, Lamborghini decided to sell his business, and it was the SAME group of Trevigliano that bought it.

Munktell, Bolinder, Volvo, Valmet and Valtra!

In the last ten years Valtra UK has grown from a small company selling a handful of machines to a company that plays an important role in farming British and Irish fields.

Valtra's story is complicated but probably starts with the Munktell family business, which joined with Bolinder to create Bolinder-Munktell in Sweden in 1932.

The Volvo car company bought Bolinder-Munktell in the 1950s and introduced their innovative 'hot bulb' engines in 1952. Intially, both the green BM tractors and red Volvo tractors were produced, but from 1958 onwards they were all painted red, and the brand name was changed to Volvo BM in 1973.

The Finish manufacturer, Valmet, bought out the tractor concern from Volvo and started producing vehicles under the Volvo BM Valmet badge in 1979.

The recession in the early 1990s hit hard, and the company had to be split, with tractors taking on the Valtra name. Today Valtra is part of the huge AGCO Corporation.

JCB

The JCB company takes its initials from the founder's name, J. C. Bamford. It is based in Rocester in Staffordshire, and manufactures equipment for the construction, demolition and agricultural industries. It is possibly the last remaining all-British tractor company in the UK.

Starting off in a lock-up garage in Uttoxeter on a shoestring, JCB is now a thriving and very successful business. The JCB Fastrac entered production in 1991 and remains in development today.

The Fastrac marked a significant milestone in tractor production. It was one of the first machines to feature proper suspension and be capable of travelling at higher than normal speeds on roads.

1953 – present

Massey Ferguson

Massey Ferguson has been the world's leading tractor brand since the 1950s. This is unsurprising, given the company's unsurpassed track record for producing original and innovative machinery – be it combines, tractors or agricultural implements.

The MF 8732 model – one of the powerful and fuel efficient 8700 series introduced in 2014.

The MF 8737 is the most powerful model in the 8700 range and makes good use of its six-cylinder, 8.4 litre power plant.

Challenger

The origins of the Challenger's unique track system date back to 1911, when UK-based Richard Hornsby & Sons of Grantham sold its innovative track system to the Holt Manufacturing Company in America (a predecessor of Caterpillar).

Produced in 1986, the Challenger Tractor was the world's first rubber-tracked agricultural tractor.

The MT800C Series comprises the latest machines to come out of the Challenger brand.

Equipped with the most advanced engine technology, these tractors are incredibly versatile and succeed in meeting the strictest engine emission regulations while retaining performance.

Fendt

Fendt is the latest manufacturer to sign up to 'Ubisense', a Cambridge-based technology company which counts Jaguar and Land Rover among its clients. The company's 3D tracking system – in which tags are attached to parts during production – is speeding up manufacture across the globe. Ultimately, this streamlines the production of Fendt tractors.

Claas Tractors

In spring 2014, Claas celebrated ten years of tractor expansion in the UK. The first Claas tractor was sold in Britain in 2004 and since then the company's position in the UK market has grown.

Claas was originally well known for its combine harvesters and balers, until the company bought out the Renault tractor concern in 2008. Over a very short space of time the company has established itself as a leading tractor manufacturer throughout Europe, offering a choice of 34 models between 72 and 524 horsepower.

Renault already had a substantial tractor fleet but Claas have wasted no time in improving not only the technology but also the variety of machines it offers. The company now caters for all sorts of agricultural needs worldwide, and its lime-green machines can often be spotted in the British countryside.

6 Robots, Precision Farming and Smart Machines

Designers of agricultural machinery are always coming up with new ways to make their products even more efficient – from the early days of Cyrus McCormick and his mechanical reaper, to the present day when the new buzz words are 'robotics' and 'precision farming'.

As ever, these innovations are likely to divide the farming community – some are eager to experiment with these technological opportunities, while others prefer to continue using more traditional methods.

It is easy to understand why many might approach these experiments with scepticism. Nevertheless, modern technology is already making its presence felt in the British agricultural market. For example, Harper Adams, a respected agricultural university based in Shropshire, has created a 'National Centre for Precision Farming' (NCPF).

The NCPF aims both to help farmers apply precision methods and give visitors an understanding of how food production could be organized in the future.

With these new farming methods becoming more mainstream, many may wonder whether this is the end of the line for the traditional tractor. Tractors as we know them are probably going to be with us for a while

longer yet, but it looks as if they will increasingly have to share the marketplace with sleeker, smarter machinery.

These developments are also being driven by a need to find more sustainable ways to grow food. Climate change is now a reality, and its effects are being felt all around the globe. The agricultural industry is waking up to the fact that, if we do not alter farming methods in accordance with these changes, we could face food shortages in the not so distant future. Robot-style machines, for instance, could be used to tend crops – their vision systems, laser sensors and satellite positioning would collect information on particular plants, creating an extensive database that could then be used to recognize the onset of certain diseases in crops.

A 'smart sprayer' would then locate and eliminate the diseased plants, effectively, yet sustainably, dealing with the issue in a way that mass spraying never could.

An increasing number of 'farmbots' are also being developed for use in the UK. These robotic machines will be capable of carrying out complicated jobs – such as hoeing weeds or pruning. American designers are similarly testing the potential of flying drones, which could be used for surveillance or even herding livestock.

While some of these machines smack of *Star Wars*, these technological advances – many of which are already with us – promise to transform the way we farm in the future.

Driverless Tractors

It's always pretty awesome watching a huge combine tackling a field of fully grown corn, the tractor slowly edging its way beside it as the crop bursts from the long arm of the combine to land in the trailer. But it's even more amazing when, suddenly, you realize that no one is actually driving the tractor!

This futuristic type of farming is happening right now. Kinze Manufacturing, an American company, has recently demonstrated its new 'Autonomous Harvest System' and shown how the combine can successfully fill up the trailer

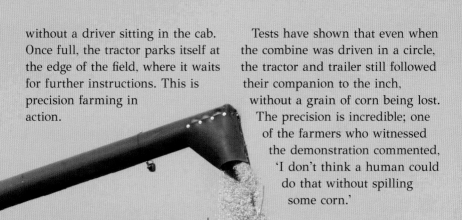

without a driver sitting in the cab. Once full, the tractor parks itself at the edge of the field, where it waits for further instructions. This is precision farming in action.

Tests have shown that even when the combine was driven in a circle, the tractor and trailer still followed their companion to the inch, without a grain of corn being lost. The precision is incredible; one of the farmers who witnessed the demonstration commented, 'I don't think a human could do that without spilling some corn.'

SPIRIT

When you read the mechanical spec for this new machine – twin 202 horsepower diesel engines, ground traction control, dynamic braking – it could describe a new, super, hi-tech sports car. In fact, it is the latest farm vehicle being tested by the Autonomous Tractor Corporation of North Dakota.

The SPIRIT is designed as a year-round helper and will tackle such jobs as tilling, combining, hauling and even mowing. It is part of the 'Autonomous Farming System' and doesn't have a driver in the usual sense.

The farmer trains and directs the autonomous vehicle with an iPad or iPhone while seated in his truck at the edge of the field. The vehicle itself is controlled by a sophisticated Artificial Intelligence System capable of replacing all the functions contributed by a human operator.

The safety controllers use a LIDAR (Light Detection and Ranging) collision avoidance system, and a perimeter ultrasonic sensor to keep the vehicle safe. To map and control the vehicle's path, two APS (Area Positioning System) controllers are used. Their inputs are compared for accuracy and also verified by the position derived from GNSS (Global Navigation Satellite System) instrumentation.

If the vehicle comes across any obstructions or indicates that there is a danger in its programmed path, the SPIRIT will shut down immediately and send a message back to the farmer.

There is high resolution video communication with the vehicle at all times.

The 'frame' is very flexible; it can house 1 to 3 power units, depending on how much power is required for the implement being used.

These are just a few of the features of this amazing new piece of farming equipment. Without a doubt, this machine is helping to lead farming technology into the future.

Alternative Fuels

With the price of petrol escalating each year, it is difficult to see how farmers can continue to pay ever larger amounts of money for their fuel. Because of this, companies are investigating ways to cut fuel costs.

Many of the larger tractor manufacturers are investigating new ways of fuelling the modern tractor and they are not short of ideas. Some of these are not necessarily all that new but are now becoming more viable. For example, there has recently been a lot of noise in the automobile industry about the potential of

fuel cell technology, yet Allis-Chalmers developed a fuel cell tractor back in the 1950s!

Then there is biogas and biofuels, new diesel electric tractors that are already on the market and, of course, solar energy and wood fuel.

These last two sound a bit odd but why not have a cab with solar panels on the roof?

Although not much development has been carried out recently, wood was used as an alternative vehicle fuel as far back as the First World War.

Future Fuels

Farming is a never-ending cycle of sowing, growing and harvesting, and this means that agricultural biomass can truly be called 'renewable energy'. Biomass will be with us for as long as farmers continue to cultivate the land. If we cultivate biomass technology, we will not need to worry about dwindling resources or finite supplies.

As early as 2010, La Bellotta Farm in Italy was chosen by New Holland Agriculture to be their pilot 'Energy Independent Farm'. It is also a perfect test-ground for the hydrogen-fuelled New Holland NH2 tractor. Trials for the second generation of the hydrogen tractor started at the farm in 2012.

Electric future

Ruben Abajo, a product marketing manager at John Deere, believes that 'Electric motors are 90 per cent efficient and electric power is safer and more flexible. It's the trend of the future.'

John Deere's 6210RE tractor went on the market in the spring of 2014. A small Swiss company (Rigitrac) has also been building low volume hydraulic-drive tractors. In 2012 it produced the EWD120 Diesel-Electric tractor, which is driven by four electric 33 kW motors, one in each of its four wheels. Its all-wheel steering allows farmers to tackle tight turning circles with ease. The power is transmitted via an 85 kW generator, which is directly connected to the 91 kW diesel engine. The steering is also extremely flexible and allows plenty of options for both rear and front axles. It has no transmission or drivetrain as such and can reach speeds of up to 40 kph.

Biofuels

As supplies of fossil-based diesel start to decrease, farmers need to look for more environmentally-friendly fuels. Biofuel is a viable alternative. Made from rapeseed oil and other vegetable oils, it can be used in many normal diesel engines. The John Deere 8530 pictured here is fully capable of running on pure biodiesel.

Deere is also pioneering the use of new agricultural technologies – it has created the first commercially available system for hands-free driving and implement operation in the field, including fully automatic headland turns.

Picture Credits

The majority of pictures are taken from the author's personal archive, but thanks also goes to the following individuals and organisations for their kind help:

Andrew Morland: 62/63, 83, 97, 98, 103B, 114T, 116, 117, 121, 136/137B; John Deere/ASM Public Relations, UK; AGCO Corporation; Claas; CNH; JCB, UK; Ford UK; SAME Deutz-Fahr; ARGO SpA; Kubota; Kinze Manufacturing, USA: 212/213; Autonomous Tractor Corp., North Dakota, USA: 214/215; Grant Thornburg: 215B; Rigitrac, Switzerland: 220–221; US Library of Congress, Washington DC, USA; Peter Brotherhood Ltd, Peterborough, Cambridgeshire, UK; Roy Chadwick for the historic Ivel images.